BRAIN WAVES

SCIENCE IN THE NATIONAL CURRICULUM FOR UPPER JUNIORS

Alan Ward

Illustration by Eric Jones.
Handwriting by Morag Tweddle.
Cover design by Hybert Design & Type.
Cover Photograph by Rob Atkins, The Image Bank.

First published 1990 by Folens Limited, Dunstable and Dublin.

ISBN 1 85276045-1   Printed by Craft Print Pte Ltd, Singapore

Folens Limited, Albert House, Apex Business Centre, Boscombe Road, Dunstable LU5 4RL, England.

How BRAIN WAVES Upper Junior Science fits in with the NATIONAL CURRICULUM

PAGE	ACTIVITY	AT(S)	LEVEL(S)	PAGE	ACTIVITY	AT(S)	LEVEL(S)
4	Fossil Factory	2(ii)	4	24	Hot Spots	3(i)	4
5	Follow That Ant!	2(i)	4	25	A Watery Adventure	3(iv)	4
6	Key Notes	2(ii)	5	26	Brilliant Idea	4(iii)	4
7	Food Chains	2(iv)	5	27	Smash Hits	4(iii)	5
8	Good Health	2(i)	4	28	Feeling The Force	4(iii)	5
9	Money For Old Smoke	2(iii)	4	29	Paper Pillar	4(iii)	5
10	Joint Operation	2(i)	5	30	Slip And Grip	4(iii)	4
11	Bony Parts	2(i)	4	31	Speed Trials	4(iii)	6
12	You Are What You Eat!	2(i)	5	32	Lighting Delights	4(i)	5
3	Eaters' Digest	2(i)	5	33	Home Computer	4(i)	6
14	Small Hands, Big Hands	2(ii)	4	34	Energy Detective	4(ii)	4
15	Science Fiction	2(ii)	5	35	Sound Puzzles	4(iv)	5
16	Wasteful You	2(iii)	4	36	Sound Sense	4(iv)	5
17	Planning Proposal	2(iii)	4	37	Magic Shadows	4(iv)	4
18	Property Values	3(i)	4	38	Bouncing Beams	4(iv)	5
19	Crazy Matters	3(i)	5	39	Space Mission	4(v)	5
20	Acid Tests	3(iii)	5	40	Orange Moon	4(v)	4
21	Does Air Weigh Anything?	3(i)	4	41	Beans And Bugs	4(ii)	6
22	Ball Of Fire	3(iii)	5	42	Think Again	4(ii)	5
23	Atomic Theory	3(i)	6				

Sheets 43 - 48   Teachers' Notes

INTRODUCTION

Brain Waves Science - Upper Junior is an essential resource of quick, safe and simple ideas to assist primary teachers who wish to integrate science activities into their day-to-day teaching. The activities it contains are lively, imaginative and up to date, often experimental, and involve children working singly or in groups. They will encourage children to share in discussions and promote concern for how science and technology affect the environment and the lives of other people.

With few exceptions, the activities are designed to take place within an hour, using the minimum of preparation and materials.

The content of the activities is inspired by the Programmes of Study for Key Stage 2 of the National Curriculum for England and Wales. It was thought that a few more challenging optional activities should be provided. These will be found on sheets 23, 31, 33 and 41.

The style of the activities is inspired by the approach to teaching science emphasised in the description of Attainment Target 1 (Scientific Investigation):

"Pupils should carry out investigations in which they:

i.   ask questions, predict and hypothesize
ii.   observe, measure and manipulate variables
iii.   interpret their results and evaluate scientific evidence."

Science in the National Curriculum. HMSO 1991.

Children should acquire scientific knowledge and understanding through observation, questioning, fair testing and by basing inferences on evidence made available from a range of sources. Users of **Brain Waves Science - Upper Junior** will find a wide variety of activities to help them achieve these aims.

Brain Waves Science - Upper Junior activities offer material relevant to many primary classroom topics, including the following:

TOPIC	RELEVANT ACTIVITY SHEETS
Minibeasts	5, 6, 7, 15, 41
Houses and homes	16, 18, 29, 32, 34
Toys	26, 27, 29, 30, 31, 32
Sports and games	8, 10, 11, 12, 19, 26, 27, 30, 31, 37
The zoo	6
Life long ago	4
Earth and space	28, 37, 38, 39, 40
Hot and cold	16, 21, 22, 24, 34
Seeds and plants	7, 41
Electricity at home	32, 34
Life underground	4, 5, 6, 25
The factory	16, 17, 18, 29, 36
The seaside	25, 31
Growing up	8, 9, 11, 12, 13, 14
Bicycles	10, 11, 18, 26, 27, 29, 30, 31, 32, 34
Seeing better	32, 37, 38
Ponds and rivers	17, 20, 22, 25
Bridges	18, 29
Communication	31, 32, 33, 35, 36, 38, 40

FOSSIL FACTORY

Key Facts

Nobody has ever actually seen a live dinosaur.
We know about dinosaurs from fossils.

Fossils are found in some kinds of rocks.
They are the remains or imprints of animals and plants that lived millions of years ago.

You NEED:
plasticine
shallow plastic bowl
soil and water
shells, chicken bones, leaves etc.
stick
spoon
ruler
paper and pencil

Model fossils

1. An easy way to make an imprint is to press a coin or a key into a layer of Plasticine.
2. Try making a thick soup of mud in the plastic bowl.
   Add soil and water, a little at a time.
   Stir the mixture with a stick, while you add a few shells, small bones, leaves and feathers.

Don't make a mess!

A thick soup of mud, about 10 centimetres deep, will do.
Spoon out the surplus water.
Let the mud dry. Perhaps it will take a week.

Carefully break apart the dried mud.
Discover your "fossils" in the "rock".

Here is a picture of a fossil leaf. The picture is half the size of the real fossil.
Measure the picture carefully and then draw the fossil leaf full-size.

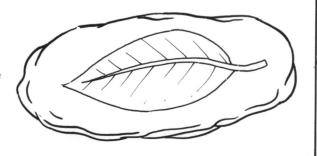

FOLLOW THAT ANT!

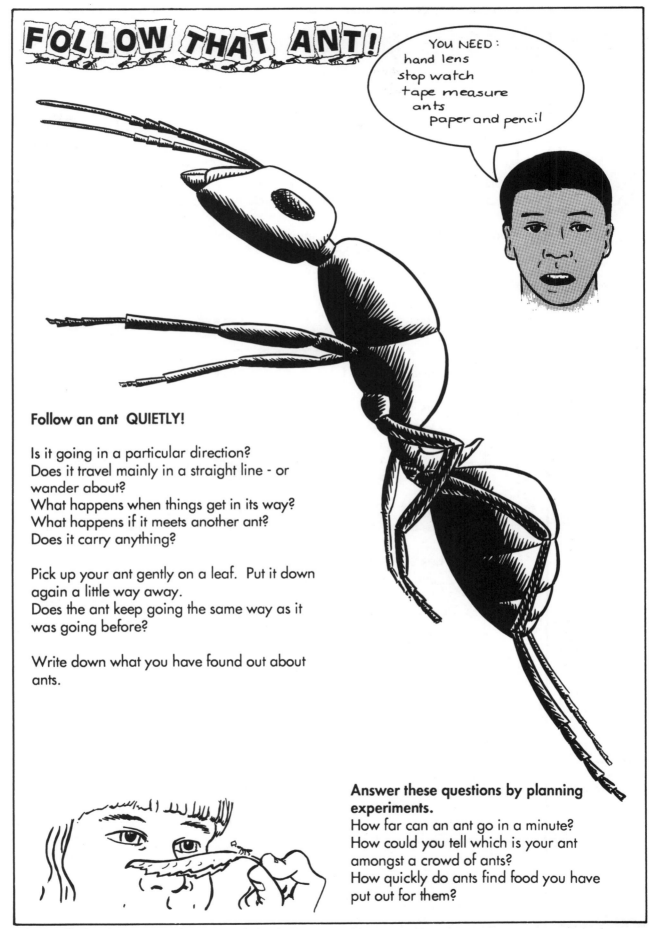

YOU NEED:
hand lens
stop watch
tape measure
ants
paper and pencil

Follow an ant QUIETLY!

Is it going in a particular direction?
Does it travel mainly in a straight line - or wander about?
What happens when things get in its way?
What happens if it meets another ant?
Does it carry anything?

Pick up your ant gently on a leaf. Put it down again a little way away.
Does the ant keep going the same way as it was going before?

Write down what you have found out about ants.

Answer these questions by planning experiments.
How far can an ant go in a minute?
How could you tell which is your ant amongst a crowd of ants?
How quickly do ants find food you have put out for them?

Key Notes

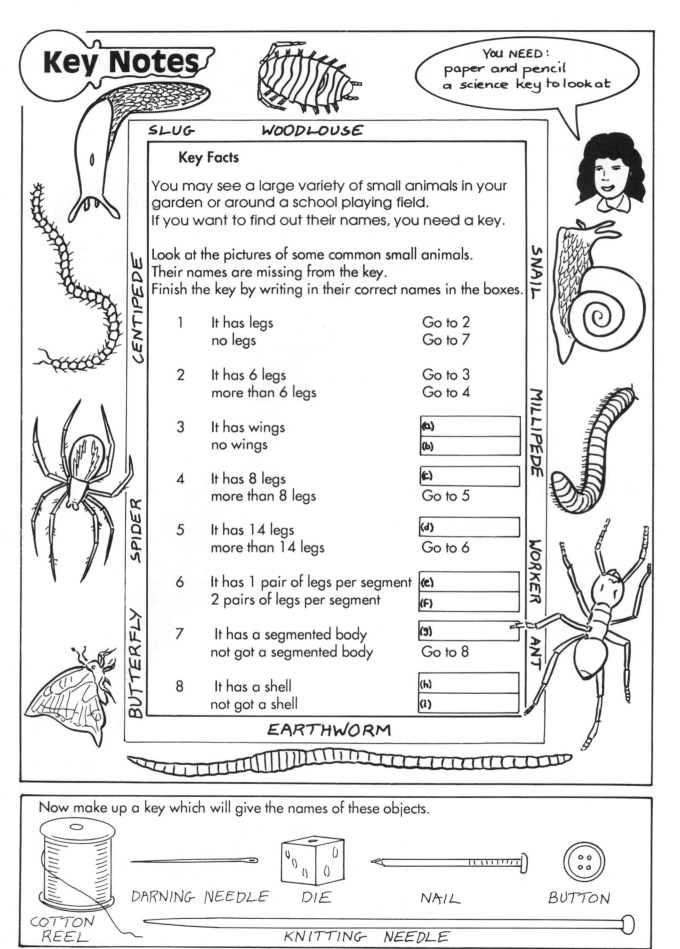

SLUG

WOODLOUSE

YOU NEED:
paper and pencil
a science key to look at

Key Facts

You may see a large variety of small animals in your garden or around a school playing field.
If you want to find out their names, you need a key.

Look at the pictures of some common small animals.
Their names are missing from the key.
Finish the key by writing in their correct names in the boxes.

1	It has legs	Go to 2
	no legs	Go to 7
2	It has 6 legs	Go to 3
	more than 6 legs	Go to 4
3	It has wings	(a)
	no wings	(b)
4	It has 8 legs	(c)
	more than 8 legs	Go to 5
5	It has 14 legs	(d)
	more than 14 legs	Go to 6
6	It has 1 pair of legs per segment	(e)
	2 pairs of legs per segment	(f)
7	It has a segmented body	(g)
	not got a segmented body	Go to 8
8	It has a shell	(h)
	not got a shell	(i)

CENTIPEDE

SPIDER

BUTTERFLY

SNAIL

MILLIPEDE

WORKER ANT

EARTHWORM

Now make up a key which will give the names of these objects.

DARNING NEEDLE

DIE

NAIL

BUTTON

COTTON REEL

KNITTING NEEDLE

FOOD CHAINS

Key Facts

When a cat eats a bird that has fed on plant berries, you could say that the cat has got some of its food from a plant.

We call this a **food chain**.

All food chains start with green plants. Green plants are the only living things that can make food from very simple chemicals

You NEED: only paper and a pencil

BERRIES ON A PLANT	BLACKBIRD	CAT

CATERPILLAR   DEER

SNAIL   OWL

YOU   GRASS (including seeds)

FIELDMOUSE   RABBIT

LETTUCE   FOX

Make up a drawing to show how these animals and plants depend upon each other for their food.

Predators eat other animals.
Which of the animals in your picture are predators?

Prey are animals that are eaten by predators.
Which of the animals in your picture are prey?

GOOD HEALTH

Grown-ups usually value good health more than anything else.

What do you think they mean by 'good health'?

Make up your own list of 7 rules for healthy living.

Your mother has a severe cold.

What should she do?

What could you do for her?

MONEY FOR OLD SMOKE

A person spends £5 a week on smoking cigarettes.
How much would that person save in a year by not smoking?

If you had that much money to spend all at once, what would you buy?

Imagine that a good friend of yours has just started to smoke regularly. Write a letter to them that gives reasons why they should stop. Add some pictures to show them what might happen if they carry on.

JOINT OPERATION

Think carefully about which body joints you use for the six movements in the chart below.
Then put ticks in the correct boxes on the chart.

JOINT	SITTING	WRITING	WALKING	JUMPING	CYCLING	SWIMMING
NECK						
SHOULDER						
ELBOW						
WRIST						
FINGER						
HIP						
KNEE						
ANKLE						
TOE						

You NEED:
scissors
glue
paper

BONY PARTS

Can you identify the bones in your skeleton?

Cut out the skeleton picture and the names of the bones. Can you put them next to the correct numbered circles on your skeleton?

| HUMERUS |
| PELVIS (hip) |
| PATELLA (kneecap) |
| DIGITS (fingers) |
| SKULL |
| FIBULA (2nd shin bone) |
| RIBS |
| RADIUS |
| SCAPULA (shoulder blade) |
| FEMUR (thigh bone) |
| BACKBONE |
| TIBIA (1st shin bone) |
| ULNA |
| CLAVICLE (collar bone) |
| STERNUM (breast bone) |
| DIGITS (toes) |

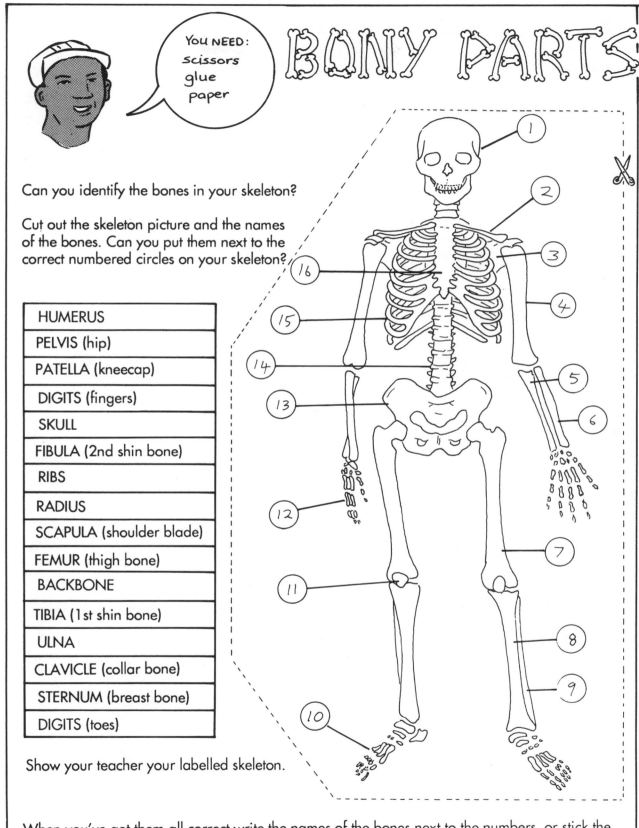

Show your teacher your labelled skeleton.

When you've got them all correct write the names of the bones next to the numbers, or stick the labels next to the correct numbers.
Now you should be able to name the bones for yourself.
Test your partner by holding one of your bones and asking them to name it.

YOU ARE WHAT YOU EAT!

You NEED:
only paper and a pencil

Key Facts

Your diet is the food you eat.
It provides your body with energy, growth and general good health.

There are three main food groups

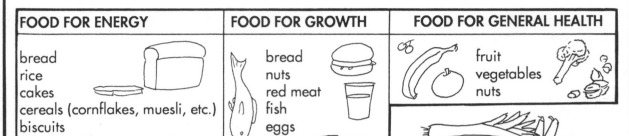

FOOD FOR ENERGY	FOOD FOR GROWTH	FOOD FOR GENERAL HEALTH
bread rice cakes cereals (cornflakes, muesli, etc.) biscuits sugar and fat (not too much)	bread nuts red meat fish eggs milk	fruit vegetables nuts

You also need fibre from wholemeal bread, fruit, vegetables and nuts.
Fibre helps with your digestion.

Don't forget **WATER**, as well, to help dissolve the food you eat.

A balanced diet consists of foods chosen from each group.

Make up a healthy menu for an average day. Be imaginative!

EATERS' DIGEST

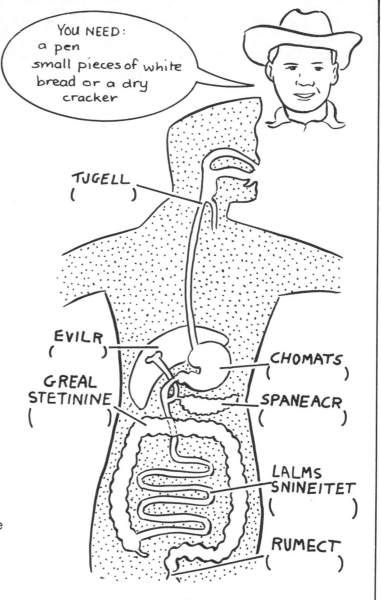

YOU NEED:
a pen
small pieces of white bread or a dry cracker

Labels to unscramble:

TJGELL ( )

EVILR ( )

CHOMATS ( )

GREAL STETININE ( )

SPANEACR ( )

LALMS SNINEITET ( )

RUMECT ( )

Key Facts

Before your body can use food it must break down the food into very tiny bits. This is called digestion.

Digestion must happen before food can move into your blood. The blood takes digested food to body parts where it is needed.

Digestion starts in your mouth.

Bread contains a food called starch that supplies energy. But starch must be changed into a kind of sugar, before it can dissolve.

Special areas of your mouth make a juice that changes starch into sugar.

Most digested food goes into the blood through the small intestine. Waste food leaves the rectum when you go to the toilet.

Here is a picture of the "food pipe" that runs down through your body. Can you name its parts by unscrambling the words?

Put a piece of white bread in your mouth. Chew it well for a minute or two.
Describe what you notice as you chew the bread..then swallow it.

SMALL HANDS. BiG HANDS.

The size of children's hands in your class will not be the same. It will vary.
Who has the biggest and smallest hands in your class?
Here is one way to find out.

Spread your fingers.
Cover the squares with your hand.
Draw around your palm and fingers.
The area of each square is one square
centimetre (1 sq. cm.)
Count the squares inside the hand outline.
Only count a square if more than half of it is covered.

YOU NEED:
a pencil
some glass
marbles

The area of the palm of my hand (in square centimetres) is: ⬚ Sq.Cm.

Compare this with the results of other children. You might be able to draw a bar chart of everyone's results on squared paper. That will show you how much the hand sizes vary.

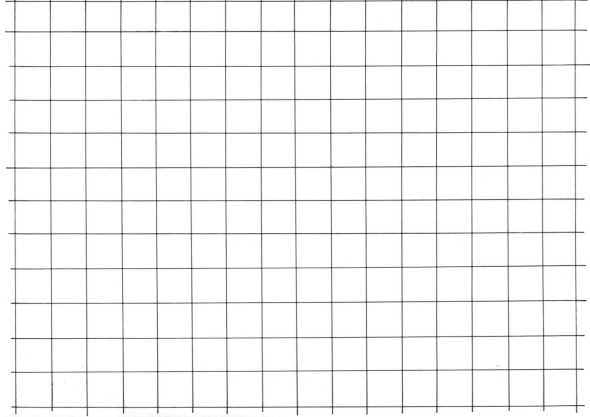

See if you can find answers to these problems.

Are both your hands the same size?
Can the biggest hands hold the most marbles?

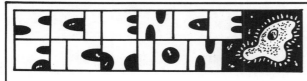 

Key Facts

The bodies of all living things including you, are built from very tiny "living bricks" that we call cells. You need a microscope to see them clearly. Each of us is made of many millions of cells. Inside the cells are sets of instructions that tell the plant or animal or microbe how to grow. The smallest instructions are called **genes**.

When living things breed, they pass on their genes to their offspring.

Imagine that a brilliant scientist has put a special gene into a microbe. This gene makes it possible for the microbe to feed on plastic. Write about some of the things (good as well as bad) that might happen if offspring from the microbe escape from the scientist's laboratory, into your home.

Draw a picture of the microbe here. Give it a name.

You NEED: only a pencil

Starting from when you arrive at school and finishing just before you go home, use this chart to record a tick for every item you throw away.

PAPER AND CARDBOARD	PLASTIC	METAL	OTHER MATERIALS (NAME THEM)

TOTALS

Compare your chart with charts made by other children in your class.
What will probably happen to this rubbish?
Which sorts of waste can be saved and used again?
What can you do to become a less wasteful person?

PLANNING PROPOSAL

YOU NEED: only a pencil

A developer wants to build a factory on an empty site in the middle of the housing estate were you live.

Give 3 reasons why you think this might be a good idea.

1. _____

2. _____

3. _____

Give 3 reasons why you think that this idea is a bad one.

1. _____

2. _____

3. _____

Draw a map in this space to show how you would use the land.

Write a few sentences to make your idea clear.

PROPERTY VALUES

YOU NEED: only a pencil

Key Facts

All materials have properties.
They have certain features which help us to identify them.
For example: iron is magnetic, but wood is not.
The properties of materials enable us to use them for special purposes.

Look around you for materials which have the properties listed on the chart.
Write in the names of the materials you find.
Also, write in uses for these materials that depend on their properties.

PROPERTY	MATERIAL	USE
HARD	Iron (example)	for making nails.
SOFT		
STRONG		
WEAK		
FLEXIBLE		
INFLEXIBLE		
SOLUBLE (In water)		
INSOLUBLE		
TRANSPARENT		
OPAQUE		

What uses can you think of for a housebrick?

CRAZY MATTERS

Professor Krakpott has invented a completely invisible form of rubber. Think of a name for this remarkable material and write a paragraph about how Krakpott might use it. (His uses can be serious, or just for fun...!)

Now Krakpott has invented an indestructible ball that will always bounce up higher than where it fell from. Write a paragraph about what you think might happen when Krakpott tests this invention.

Here are a couple of riddles for you!

What gets wetter the more it dries?

What holds water, yet is full of holes?

ACID TESTS

Key Facts

Chemists want to know if a chemical is an acid or an alkali.
Some foods and medicines are acids.
Others are alkalis.
Acids taste sour and alkalis taste bitter.
Never taste any substance until you know it is safe.

Indicators are used to indicate whether a substance is an acid or an alkali.
An indicator called litmus is used to make test papers.
Blue litmus paper turns pink or red when it is dipped in an acid.
Red litmus paper turns bluish when it is dipped in an alkali.

YOU NEED:
red and blue litmus paper strips
vinegar
soap
milk of magnesia
lemon juice
4 saucers
water
spoon
piece of limestone
a pencil

Put the substances you have been given into separate saucers.
Dip a piece of litmus strip into each of the substances.
Fill in the spaces in this chart with what you see.

SUBSTANCE TESTED	RESULT WITH RED LITMUS	RESULT WITH BLUE LITMUS	ACID OR ALKALI ?
VINEGAR			
SOAP			
MILK OF MAGNESIA			
LEMON JUICE			

Gases from power stations that burn coal or oil and from motorcar exhausts get into the damp air and cause **ACID RAIN.**
Spoon a little vinegar on to the piece of limestone.
What do you see?

_____

How might acid rain pollution cause damage in your town?

_____

_____

DOES AIR WEIGH ANYTHING?

Stand in bare feet next to the closed door of the refrigerator.
Open the door. You should be able to feel cold air on your feet.

Wet the back of one hand.
Ask somebody to take out an empty food storage box from the refrigerator.
Get them to tip the box over your wet wrist.
What do you notice?

Why does your observation suggest that air weighs something?

YOU NEED:
a refrigerator
a hot radiator or other safe source of heat
cotton
scissors

Do these activities with an adult

Many children say that hot air rises.
Cut out the curly snake on this sheet. Make a hole through "X". Dangle your snake from a thread.
Hold the curly snake over a radiator.
What happens to the snake?

If heated air is rising, what must be happening to colder air around it?

Why does your observation suggest that air weighs something?

Supermarkets do not always cover cold-storage boxes of food.
How do your experiments help to explain why?

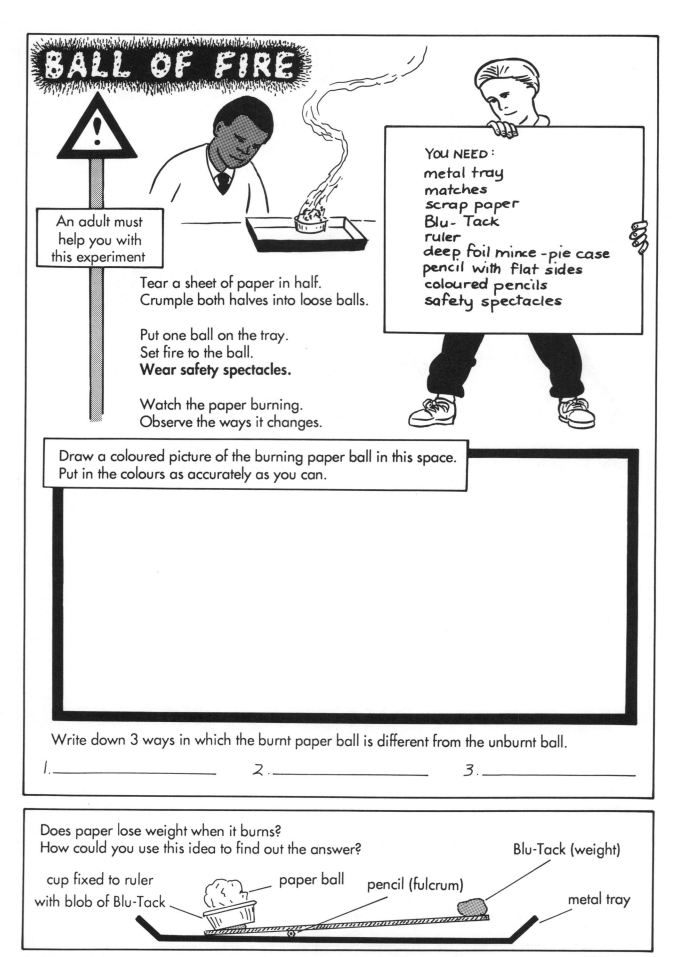

BALL OF FIRE

An adult must help you with this experiment

YOU NEED:
metal tray
matches
scrap paper
Blu-Tack
ruler
deep foil mince-pie case
pencil with flat sides
coloured pencils
safety spectacles

Tear a sheet of paper in half.
Crumple both halves into loose balls.

Put one ball on the tray.
Set fire to the ball.
Wear safety spectacles.

Watch the paper burning.
Observe the ways it changes.

Draw a coloured picture of the burning paper ball in this space.
Put in the colours as accurately as you can.

Write down 3 ways in which the burnt paper ball is different from the unburnt ball.

1. _____ 2. _____ 3. _____

Does paper lose weight when it burns?
How could you use this idea to find out the answer?

cup fixed to ruler with blob of Blu-Tack — paper ball — pencil (fulcrum) — Blu-Tack (weight) — metal tray

ATOMIC THEORY

Tear a sheet of newspaper in half.

Tear one of the halves in half again.

Tear one of the resulting "half-halves" in half. How many times can you manage to do this before the pieces are too small to tear?.

YOU NEED:
pencil and paper
newspaper
lump of sugar
glass of warm water
shoebox containing chopped onions

Key Facts

Scientists say that eventually you must get a piece that cannot be broken up this way any more.
They call this smallest piece an "atom".
Every substance is made from atoms or a collection of atoms called a "molecule".
The properties of substances are changed if their atoms or molecules are broken.

Do these activities with your teacher.

1. Stir a lump of sugar into the glass of warm water. Afterwards, taste the water. What do you notice?

2. Your teacher will open the shoe box. Wait patiently for a while ...... What do you notice?

Try to explain these observations by writing about atoms.

Late one summer evening, while lying in bed, you smell the roses in the garden.

What is your explanation?

HOT SPOTS

Spot the temperature readings on this thermometer.
Write them inside the circles.

After writing down the temperatures,
put them in the correct boxes in the chart below.

YOU NEED:
a pencil
a thermometer

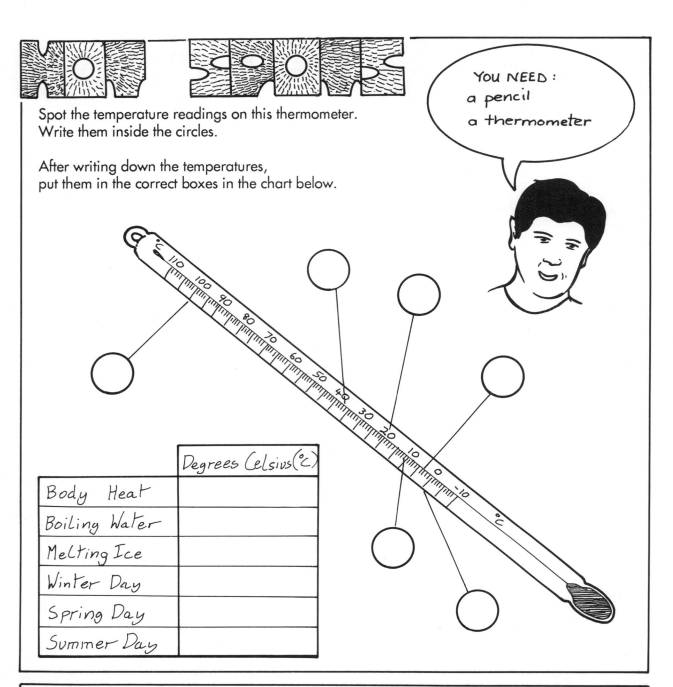

	Degrees Celsius (°C)
Body Heat	
Boiling Water	
Melting Ice	
Winter Day	
Spring Day	
Summer Day	

Here is a useful little poem, but don't take it too literally!

"5 and 10 and 21
winter, spring
and summer sun".

What do you think the
numbers mean?

Find the hottest and coldest spots in your room.

Try to work them out without a thermometer.
If you have a thermometer, test your ideas.

A WATERY ADVENTURE

YOU NEED: only a pencil

Key Facts

Water is always moving from one part of our surroundings to another.
There may be water in the rain that once formed part of the body of a dinosaur!

Imagine being a drop of water.

You could freeze into ice, or boil away as steam.
You could be part of an ice cube in the Queen's royal lemonade, or just a lonely snowflake in a terrible winter storm ....

Use the space below to describe: **"My Adventure as a Drop of Water"**

Your description should include the idea of how water can move between the land, rivers, sea, clouds and even living things!

BRILLIANT IDEA

Key Facts

The pull of gravity is useful.
Falling water can work a waterwheel and the wheel can drive a machine.

Gravity is fun!
It pulls you down a slide.
You use the force of gravity
when you roll balls down a slope,
as part of a game.

YOU NEED:
crayons or
coloured pencils

Draw a machine
or invent a fun
activity that depends
on gravity.
Keep it simple!

Describe how
your idea works
in this
space.

SMASH HITS

Make a slope by propping up one end
of a classroom table, using books.
This is the **"slow slope"**.
Mark a "start line" near the top of the slope,
and a "target line" more than halfway down.

Put the target on its line.

Roll each tin, in turn, so that it collides with the
target.

Ask a partner to catch the tins if they roll off
the table.

Measure how far the target is pushed.
Try your test three times.

Prop up the table with more books, to make
the slope steeper.
This is the **"fast slope"**

Repeat your tests with the two tins.

YOU NEED:
large tin of beans
small tin of beans
wooden block 'target'
books to support
table legs
a ruler
a pencil

Start Line

Target

SLOW SLOPE	Distance Target Moved (cm.)		
	1ST GO	2ND GO	3RD GO
Light Tin			
Heavy Tin			

FAST SLOPE	Distance Target Moved (cm.)		
	1ST GO	2ND GO	3RD GO
Light Tin			
Heavy Tin			

How is the distance that the target moves
affected by changing the weight of the tin?

How is the distance that the target moves
affected by changing the speed of the tin?

Why is it important to try each test three times
and not just once?

What lessons do these tests teach you for road safety?

A bullet does not weigh much, yet it can do
great damage. Why is this?

FEELING THE FORCE

Key Facts

The Earth holds everything down because of a "pull" that we call the 'force of gravity'.

When you weigh yourself, you are finding out how strongly the Earth's gravity is pulling on your body. You call this your "weight".

Imagine that you live on a different planet where the force of gravity pulling down on everything, including your body, is TEN TIMES MORE than on Earth.
You would weigh TEN TIMES MORE than you do now!

Think about how that would change the appearance of animals that move about on that planet.

Draw your own design for an animal that is suited to living on the new planet.

Use your imagination - but be scientific as well!

Paper Pillar

Challenge

Who can fold an A4 sheet of paper
in the shape of a free-standing pillar,
to make a support for the heaviest book?

YOU NEED:
- supply of used A4 paper
- pencil
- stapler

Here are some ways to try:

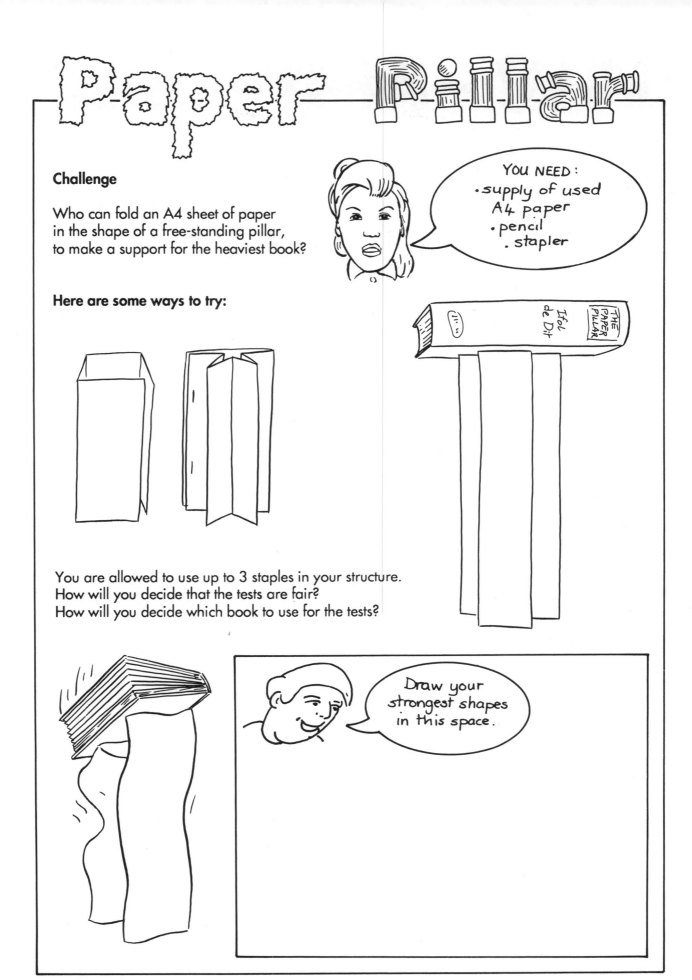

You are allowed to use up to 3 staples in your structure.
How will you decide that the tests are fair?
How will you decide which book to use for the tests?

Draw your strongest shapes in this space.

SLIP-AND-GRIP

Key Facts

Friction is a force that stops things slipping.

YOU NEED:
a music cassette case
table mat
ruler
2 rubber bands
pencil

Rest the cassette case on the smooth side of the mat.
Raise an end of the mat, until the case starts to slide.
The height gives you an idea of the friction between the case and mat.

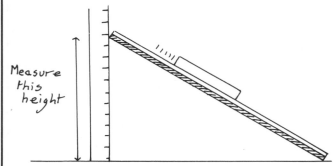

Measure this height

Measure the height of the table mat with a ruler.
Repeat the test, but use the rough side of the mat.
Fix the rubber bands longways on the cassette case.
Repeat both tests.

Fill in this chart with your measurements.

	AMOUNT OF FRICTION (Height of raised edge of mat)
Smooth slope	
Smooth slope (with rubber bands)	
Rough slope	
Rough slope (with rubber bands)	

Tell your partner what you have found out about friction.

Write down two ways that friction is useful.

1. _____

2. _____

Write down two ways that friction is a nuisance.

1. _____

2. _____

SPEED TRIALS

3 aeroplanes took off together from base. Here are their flight-paths after one hour. (Each centimetre on the sheet represents a real distance flown of 10 kilometres.)

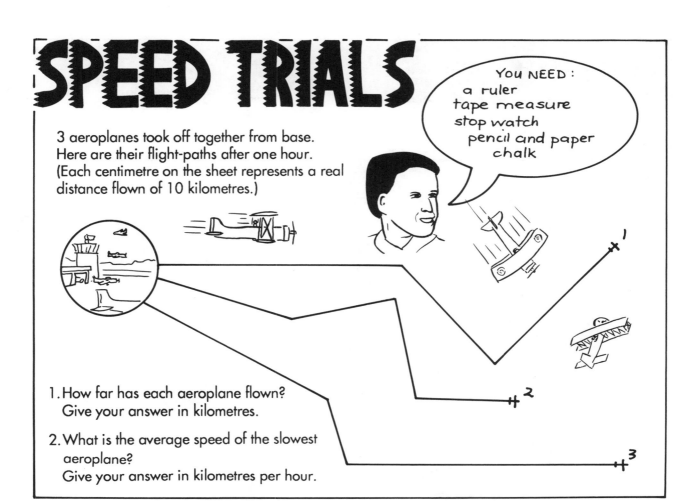

YOU NEED :
a ruler
tape measure
stop watch
pencil and paper
chalk

1. How far has each aeroplane flown? Give your answer in kilometres.

2. What is the average speed of the slowest aeroplane? Give your answer in kilometres per hour.

Let's find out how fast you can run.

You must do this activity under adult supervision.

3. How many metres can you run in 10 seconds? Plan a fair test with a friend. Time 10 seconds with a watch.
Measure the distance you run with a tape measure. Some chalk might come in handy. Your partner can have a go and then you can each repeat the test once more - if you aren't out of breath!

4. What is the average distance you have run in 10 seconds?

5. Now work out your average speed. Divide the average distance by 10 to work the speed out in metres per second.

6. What is that average speed in kilometres per hour?

HINT
To answer this question . . .
You need to work out how many seconds there are in one hour, and you need to know how many metres there are in one kilometre.

Look at these circuits.

YOU NEED:
some paper
and a pencil

Fill in this chart with a tick for each circuit.

	1	2	3	4	5	6	7	8	9	10	11	12	13
The lights are 'on' in these circuits													
The lights are 'off' in these circuits													

Design a torch that includes a switch.

Explain how it works.

This page may be photocopied for classroom use only.

HOME COMPUTER

Key Facts

In a digital computer, information is stored as numbers made up of only two figures "0" and "1".

In most electronic computers all numbers can be represented as combinations of 'noughts' and 'ones'.

This system is called the binary system. ("Bi" means "two". You see it in the word "bicycle".)

YOU NEED:
a pencil or knitting needle
scissors
a paper punch

You are going to build a simple computer that can answer these questions.

How many boys keep dogs?
How many girls have dark hair?
How many people wear glasses?
How many dog owners have dark hair?

This activity will give you a rough idea of how this system works.

Instead of using the numerals "0" and "1", we shall use the answers "yes" and "no" to certain questions:

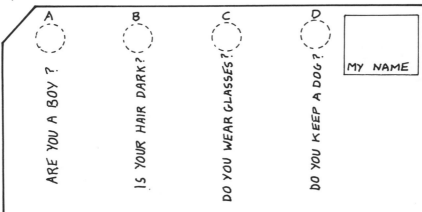

A — ARE YOU A BOY?
B — IS YOUR HAIR DARK?
C — DO YOU WEAR GLASSES?
D — DO YOU KEEP A DOG?

MY NAME

This is your computer data card. Cut it out carefully.

Answer the questions on your computer data card

If your answer is YES, push your pencil through the spot, like this:

(It is much better to make a clean hole by using a paper punch)

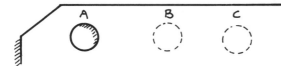

A   B   C

If your answer is NO, cut out a wide slot, like this:

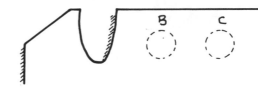

B   C

Put all your friends' computer data cards together with yours. Let your teacher have the bundle. This bundle is the computer!

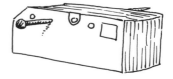

Your teacher will use a pencil or a knitting needle to answer the questions at the top of the sheet - and quite a few more!

ENERGY DETECTIVE

YOU NEED: some paper and a pencil

Can you see how energy is being wasted here?

Try to spot 10 ways in which this family could save energy.

Think of ways to save energy in your school.

Plan a school "Save Energy Week".

Plan an experiment to find out if energy had been saved by your campaign.

SAVE ENERGY

YOU NEED: only a pencil.

Jonathan sees the lightning before he hears the thunder.

Emma cannot see the speeding jet-plane in the place where its sound seems to be coming from.

Ahmed is making his voice bounce off the factory wall.

Gran says: "I've read that sound travels at 330 metres per second".

Use Gran's information to explain Jonathan's, Emma's, and Ahmed's observations in this space.

SOUND SENSE

YOU NEED: only a pencil

You will have mixed feelings about sounds.

Make two lists.

SOUNDS YOU LIKE	SOUNDS YOU DON'T LIKE

Sound we don't like in the environment is a problem.

People even talk about "noise pollution".

Do a sound survey of your neighbourhood. Perhaps your teacher will take you out.

Write the names of sounds you hear on the sound scale chart.

LOUDNESS SCALE	SOUNDS
Rustling Leaves	
Ordinary Talking	
Busy Road Traffic	
A Twin-Engined Aeroplane	
Loud Thunder	
A Jumbo-Jet Taking Off	
Firing a Field-Gun	
Launching a Spacecraft	

GETTING LOUDER

Compare your list with other children's.
Why don't you always agree?

MAGIC SHADOWS

Practice making hand-shadows on a bright, sunny day.

YOU NEED:
bright sunlight or a projector
a blank wall or a screen.

Choose one or two of these ideas.
Aim for perfection!

See if you can make your shadows move.
That's more interesting!

Invent your own "shadow magic" and share your best efforts with your friends.

BOUNCING BEAMS

Hold the first cardboard tube, so that one end touches the mirror while you look through the other end.

Get a friend to hold the second tube, with an end next to where your tube is touching the mirror.

Your friend must change the angle of his or her tube, until your eye can be seen - reflected by the mirror - through the other end.

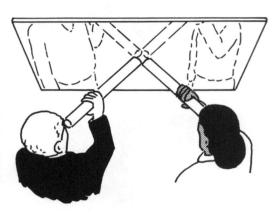

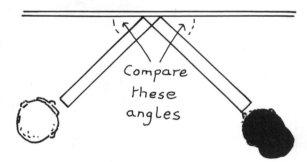

Compare these angles

Change the angle your tube makes with the mirror.

Then get your friend to change the angle of the second tube, until they can see your eye again.

Change the angle of your tube each time.

Do the test four or five times.

What do you notice about your friend's angles, compared with yours?

Use Blu-Tack to fix a tiny shiny object, such as a silver coin, to your wrist. Stick it just over your pulse.

Try to get light coming from the sun to bounce off this "mirror" and land on the ceiling. See if you can show your pulse beating.

NEVER LOOK DIRECTLY AT THE SUN!

SPACE MISSION

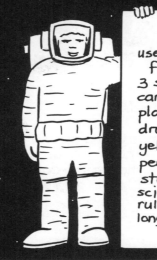

YOU NEED:
use of playing field
3 sticks
cardboard scraps
plasticine
drawing pins
yellow paint
pencil
string
scissors
ruler
long tape measure

Use the Key Facts to make scale models of the Earth, moon and sun.

Fix the "sun" to a stick, using drawing pins. Paint the model sun yellow.

Reinforce the cardboard if it flaps in the wind.

Key Facts	REAL DIAMETER	SCALE MODEL DIAMETER
EARTH	7,900 miles	1 cm. (Plasticine Ball)
MOON	2,200 miles	¼ cm. (Plasticine Ball)
SUN	865,000 miles	109 cm. (Cardboard Circle)

Distance from Earth to the moon	
REAL	SCALE
240,000 miles	30 cm.

Distance from Earth to the sun	
REAL	SCALE
93,000,000 miles	13,000 cm (120 m.)

Draw the "sun" circle (radius 54.5 cm) like this:

You might need to fix pieces of cardboard together.

Put the tiny "Earth" and "moon" models on top of separate sticks.

Use the data on distances to fix the 3 sticks in a line on the school field.

Discuss this model of part of the solar system with your teacher. What do you think of it?

How can you use your model to explain how an eclipse happens?

Challenge
Collect more data from books to make a scale model of the whole solar system.

ORANGE MOON

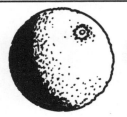

Key Facts

The moon goes around the Earth once every 29 and a half days.
You will have noticed how the moon seems to change its shape each night.
These "shapes" are called the moon's phases.
This activity will help you to understand how the moon's phases occur.

YOU NEED:
an orange or a small ball
bright sunlight or a projector

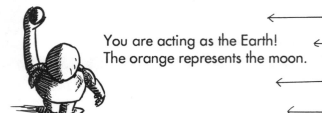

You are acting as the Earth!
The orange represents the moon.

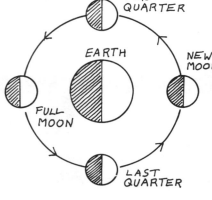

FIRST QUARTER

EARTH

NEW MOON

FULL MOON

LAST QUARTER

SUNLIGHT

Stand facing the sunlight. Hold the orange in front of you.
Don't look at the sun!

Does any direct sunlight reach the part of the orange you can see?
Keep holding the orange in front of you.
Turn 90° left.

How much direct sunlight can you see on the orange this time?
Again, turn 90° left. Now your back should be to the sun.

How much of the surface of the orange is illuminated by sunlight?
Once more, turn 90° left. How much sunlight can you see on the orange?

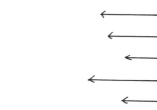

Use the pictures on this sheet to explain what you have seen.

BEANS AND BUGS

YOU NEED: only a pencil

Roddy the gardener says that beans like being tickled with a feather. He says the flowers like it so much that they produce a better crop.

Is Roddy daft, or might there be something in this tickling idea?
(**Hint**: What do you know about how flowers grow and reproduce?)

Why do you think Roddy's idea might work?

This little black bug backs away from a lighted match, so obviously it doesn't like heat. Gran, who is a scientist, disagrees with this argument.

Why do you think Gran disagrees?

THINK AGAIN

YOU NEED: only a pencil

Dylan feels hot, so he opens the refrigerator. He says it will cool the whole room.

Write about Dylan's idea in this space.

Mandy sees a light moving slowly amongst the clouds in the night sky.

She says it is a spaceship from Mars.

Write about Mandy's idea here.

TEACHERS' NOTES

FOSSIL FACTORY
Sheet 4 AT2(ii):
Fossils can sometimes be found in rocks that were formed over millions of years, from layers of mud and sand grains that sank to the bottom of swamps, lakes and seas. Ancient bones and soft body parts have generally been replaced by minerals, so the model fossils will only give a rough idea of how real fossils were formed. The children can play a game by trying to identify imprints in plasticine by touch, whilst blindfolded. The model fossil project will be carried on a week or so later, during another lesson. The measuring exercise will develop observational and scaling skills.

FOLLOW THAT ANT!
Sheet 5 AT2(i):
You are advised to have a book containing information about ants handy. A compass will be useful for telling precise directions. One way to work out how fast an ant is going is to follow its path by making chalk marks. Do this for one minute. Then rest a piece of string over the chalk marks and measure the relevant length of string. Perhaps a dot of Tippex will label an ant. You could try to feed ants with cake crumbs, sugar, jam or treacle. Common "worker" ants are wingless and sterile females. Male and female ants do have wings, like most other insects.

KEY NOTES
Sheet 6 AT2(ii):
When using a key you must always start at the beginning and go through it until you find a name. You might wish to help the children to fill in the missing names in the key given as an example.

The order of animals as they should appear in the boxes is:

(a) butterfly	(d) woodlouse	(g) earthworm
(b) worker ant	(e) centipede	(h) snail
(c) spider	(f) millipede	(i) slug

Here is a possible key for the 6 objects:

1 It has a point or points	Go to 2		4 It is round	Go to 5
no point	Go to 4		not round	DIE
2 It has one point	Go to 3		5 It has one hole	COTTON REEL
2 points	SCISSORS		4 holes	BUTTON
3 It has a hole in it	NEEDLE			
no hole	NAIL			

FOOD CHAINS
Sheet 7 AT2(iv):
Green plants contain the pigment chlorophyll that enables them to manufacture food from water, carbon dioxide gas taken from the air and various chemicals taken in by their roots. This is the process called photosynthesis. Non-green plants and animals cannot do this, so other forms of life depend upon green plants for their food. Sometimes plants are eaten directly by animals, and sometimes these animals ("primary consumers" or herbivores) are preyed upon by predatory animals ("secondary consumers" or carnivores). Real food chains are complicated and are interconnected, so it would make more sense to think about food "webs". Perhaps the children will be able to explain why animals that are higher up in the food chains (owls, foxes, etc.) are less numerous than primary consumers, such as caterpillars, snails and rabbits.

GOOD HEALTH
Sheet 8 AT2(i):
The children's lists will inspire lively and useful discussion. Items on the lists should include taking regular exercise, eating a "balanced" diet, caring for one's teeth, keeping clean, not neglecting cuts and other injuries, wearing appropriate clothing, keeping warm and fairly dry, and avoidance of harmful substances such as tobacco, alcohol and other drugs. The children could also design posters illustrating typically healthy people.

TEACHERS' NOTES

MONEY FOR OLD SMOKE
Sheet 9 AT2(iii):
Cancer of the lungs and bronchitis are more common amongst smokers. Cigarette smoke can damage the lungs' cleaning system. Furthermore, the smoking habit of some people affects the health and comfort of others, and it is a fire hazard. Yet not everybody would agree that smoking should be banned. There is no doubt, however, that smoking is unhealthy. You would probably not wish to encourage children to have an ambition to take up smoking. Enjoy a lively debate! There might even be children in your class who are allowed to smoke cigarettes when they are at home.

JOINT OPERATION
Sheet 10 AT2(i):
Get the children to appreciate how supple their bodies are, by manipulating their joints. Encourage them to put good detail into their designs. They can use the blank side of the sheet if they need more space.

BONY PARTS
Sheet 11 AT2(i):
After the children have tried to name the bones by putting the paper labels next to the numbers, tell them the correct answers. Encourage the children who fail to try again, until they get all the names right. Ask the class why they think having a skeleton is important (to enable us to stand up, for the attachment of muscles, to protect vital body parts.) Ask the children to count how many pairs of ribs there are on the skeleton (12 pairs, including 2 pairs of "floating ribs"). Point out that the so-called backbone is not one bone, but a whole series of bones joined together, to make the backbone flexible.

Answers

1	skull	5	ulna	9	fibula	13	pelvis
2	clavicle	6	radius	10	digits (toes)	14	backbone
3	scapula	7	femur	11	patella	15	ribs
4	humerus	8	tibia	12	digits (fingers)	16	sternum

YOU ARE WHAT YOU EAT!
Sheet 12 AT2(i)
These food groups will make more sense to juniors than "carbohydrates", "proteins" and "fats". Comment on the children's efforts, giving praise for imaginative ideas. Ask the children to look up the word "malnutrition" (or simply ask them what they think it might mean, before telling them). Perhaps the children will be interested in making a record of all the food they eat during one whole day at home. Ask them if they think they eat a balanced diet. The activity may be useful as part of a discussion on diets from different cultures and problems of over-consumption (sugar, salt, fats).

EATERS DIGEST
Sheet 13 AT2(i):
The children should notice that the white bread or cracker tastes sweeter as the starch is changed to sugar. You may need to help the children with the words in the puzzle. Bearing in mind that the stomach is towards the left side of the body, help the children to locate where the various organs are in their own bodies.

Answers

tugell (gullet)	greal stetinine (large intestine)
evilr (liver)	lalms snineitet (small intestine)
chomats (stomach)	rumect (rectum)
spaneacr (pancreas)	

SMALL HANDS. BIG HANDS
Sheet 14 AT2(ii):
Variation between individuals and species is important in biological studies. In this practical example the children should enjoy an element of competition. Make a tally or plot a graph of the children's results on the blackboard. Discuss whether this method is the only way, or even the "best" way to measure hand size. The game with the marbles should also be fun and can provide an opportunity for fair-testing, e.g., how should the marbles be held?

TEACHERS' NOTES

SCIENCE FICTION
Sheet 15 AT2(ii):
Presumably the escaped microbes will be able to gobble up all the waste plastics littering the environment, but what will they do to the plastic objects that we value, such as plastic window frames? Although this activity is only intended to enable children to make imaginative use of the concept of a gene, important questions should be raised for discussion. Scientists called genetic engineers can already implant genes from one species into another, but the practice of so-called genetic engineering is controversial. It will be studied in more detail in the secondary school. Bacteria have been genetically engineered to break down toxic wastes and oil spillages. Up until now there are no reports of them having become a nuisance.

WASTEFUL YOU
Sheet 16 AT2(iii):
Give out copies of the chart on the day before the survey, and make certain that the children know what they have to do. Hopefully, the children will be putting their rubbish in litter bins. The children will be pleased if you, too, fill in a chart. The main aim of this activity is to make children aware of just how much waste they produce. Another aim is to stimulate discussion about the possibilities for recycling certain kinds of waste, such as paper, rags, metal and glass.

PLANNING PROPOSAL
Sheet 17 AT2(iii):
Perhaps this exercise could be linked to a real local issue. In discussion, try to keep a balance between positive and negative arguments.

PROPERTY VALUES
Sheet 18 AT3(i):
The children's responses are going to vary a great deal and there will be much scope for discussion. Before starting, make certain that the children understand what the key words mean. Don't overlook the question at the bottom of the sheet. It could lead to a lively session of creative thinking, but have some ideas ready yourself, such as bookends, water conservers in toilet cisterns or drawing pin/paper clip holders.

CRAZY MATTERS
Sheet 19 AT3(i):
The children should have no difficulty over Krakpott's invisible rubber, but the idea of the indestructible ball is more challenging. Such a ball would be made of a material that impossibly gains energy every time it bounces. Nothing could do this. If such a ball were bounced on the floor, indoors, it might eventually smash its way through the roof, then go on bouncing further and further out into space! Eventually it might gain enough energy to smash moons and planets! The answers to the riddles are a towel and a sponge.

ACID TESTS
Sheet 20 AT3(iii):
Warn the children that acids and alkalis can cause burns and damage other materials and human skin. Eyes are especially vulnerable. Car batteries contain sulphuric acid, highly corrosive and dangerous. Substances which have no effect on indicators are called neutral substances. Acids and alkalis can be used to neutralize each other, if you mix them carefully. To demonstrate, prepare some weakened vinegar in a saucer, then add diluted milk of magnesia (or another alkali), a little at a time while stirring, until the mixture has no affect on either red or blue litmus. You can buy the finger size litmus "books" quite cheaply at a chemist's, but economise by urging the children only to use pieces of the strips for the tests.

DOES AIR WEIGH ANYTHING?
Sheet 21 AT3(i):
Cold air is (volume for volume) heavier than hot air. If we are happy to be talking about "heavier", we are obviously talking about weight - the pull of gravity on materials. When you open the refrigerator door, or tip up the food storage box containing cold air, gravity makes the air pour down. If heated air rises - to make the paper spiral spin - it is reasonable to suppose that gravity must be pulling down colder air, to replace the hot air. Cold air does not escape from uncovered supermarket cold-storage boxes, because cold air is heavier than (more strictly "denser than") the surrounding warm air.

TEACHERS' NOTES

BALL OF FIRE
Sheet 22 AT3(iii):
You might prefer to demonstrate one or both of these activities. The burnt paper is black, makes a dark, sooty stain, is thinner, more crinkled and more brittle than the unburnt paper. Encourage the children to speculate about the smoke given off. Discuss what the smoke is made of - incompletely burnt paper and carbon particles. Does the smoke pollute the air? Is there any connection with "global warming"? The carbon dioxide made when the paper burns contributes to the "greenhouse effect" by preventing heat escaping from the atmosphere. What conditions are needed for a fire? The three corners of the fire "triangle" are **fuel** (the paper), a high enough **temperature** and **oxygen** from the air. The ruler will tilt the other way soon after the paper ball is ignited, indicating loss of weight.

ATOMIC THEORY
Sheet 23 AT3(i):
Children might enjoy an element of competition in the paper-tearing activity. The sugar breaks down (dissolves) into particles (molecules) too small to be seen. These spread to every drop of water in the glass. This means that they can be tasted in any drop. Particles (molecules) from the raw onions float through the air, and eventually reach every child's nose. "Smell particles" from the roses are wafted by the night breeze into the bedroom.

HOT SPOTS
Sheet 24 AT3(i):
Body heat (37°C), boiling water (100°C), melting ice (0°C), winter day (4°C), spring day (11°C), summer day (20°C). The poem is a handy device for understanding the Celsius temperatures given in weather forecasts. Obviously, the numbers in the poem cannot be too specific.

A WATERY ADVENTURE
Sheet 25 AT3(iv):
Before you let the children write their stories, talk to them about the 3 states of matter (solid, liquid, gas) as applied to water. Ask questions about how water occurs in nature and day-to-day experience. Find out if the children are familiar with the terms "evaporation" and "condensation". Discuss the significance of water in different forms of weather, such as snowfall and vast rains that can cause destructive flooding. Emphasise the dependence of living things on water, and how water is continually recycled in nature.

BRILLIANT IDEA
Sheet 26 AT4(iii):
Discuss the force of gravity with the children. This is a pull that seems to come from the centre of the earth. When the pull of gravity on an object is measured, it is called weight. Try to inspire the children. Suggest that they make rough sketches before drawing and describing their ideas. Do remind them that they are advised to keep their inventions simple.

SMASH HITS
Sheet 27 AT4(iii):
Any moving object is said to have momentum, and therefore is capable of delivering a force if it collides with anything. Momentum is increased by both greater weight (strictly speaking, mass) and by greater speed. The implications should be clear enough for road safety. A bullet's momentum is vastly increased by its high speed, and the effects of its impact are enhanced by its metal composition and its shape. The children should appreciate that it takes longer for bicycle brakes to act, by absorbing the momentum of the vehicle, if the vehicle is travelling faster.

FEELING THE FORCE
Sheet 28 AT4(iii):
This idea is most suitable for fourth year juniors working on a topic about the planets and space exploration, but the main aim is to get children to think of gravity as a force. Since the force of gravity acting on a body changes on different planets because of their size and composition, a body's weight can change, too.

TEACHERS' NOTES

PAPER PILLAR
Sheet 29 AT4(iii):
Provide some means to weigh books from the classroom library. All the paper used must be of a "standard" quality. The children can make up as many different structures as they wish, but, for competitive testing, each child must fold a fresh (untested) model for a public demonstration.

SLIP AND GRIP
Sheet 30 AT4(iii):
Three ways that friction is useful could include a motorcar tyre tread, rough soles on shoes, and the rough surface on the side of a matchbox for striking a match. Three ways that friction is a nuisance could include the low friction of icy patches and polished floors, the slipperiness of a banana skin, and the high friction between a heavy box and the ground which makes it difficult for us to drag the box along. The tests are fairer if the case is always put on the mat in the same way, and if the rubber bands are put inside the case when they are not on the outside, so that the weight is not changed.

SPEED TRIALS
Sheet 31 AT4(iii):
The aim of this activity is to reinforce the idea that speed is distance travelled in a certain time. It might be possible for you to supervise a small group of children doing the running trials in the school playground.
Warn the children about any hazards to safety.

LIGHTING DELIGHTS
Sheet 32 AT4(i):
Bulbs being lit (1, 2, 4, 7, 8, 10, 12, 13). Bulbs not being lit (3, 5, 6, 9, 11). You can, of course, have some 1.5 volt batteries, 1.25 volt bulbs and wires handy to check the circuits, if you are in any doubt. When the children are sure of the correct answer, they can crayon the lit bulbs yellow.

HOME COMPUTER
Sheet 33 AT4(i):
This model will give an impression of how an electronic computer, programmed with information "stored" in binary numbers, can process information. **Example:** Say you want to find the names of all boys in the class who keep pet dogs. Poke the pencil through holes lettered **A**. Lift all these "boys cards". Leave the other cards behind in your hand. Put them aside. Poke the pencil through holes lettered **D** on the bundle of "boys cards". Lift out all the "keep a dog" cards in this bundle. Discard the data cards that are left behind. Now, hanging on your pencil, you will have only the cards naming the boys in your class who keep dogs. It should not be difficult to work out how to obtain names with other specifications. Try all the light-haired girls who don't wear glasses and who don't have pet dogs. When the children understand how the "computer" is operated, let them use it to answer their own questions.

ENERGY DETECTIVE
Sheet 34 AT4(ii):
Switch off the light. Turn off the taps (to conserve energy at the waterworks). Turn down the thermostat on the radiator. The people could wear warmer clothes. Unplug the small heater. Shut the window, switch off the kettle, turn off the TV, close the cat-flap, switch off the torch. Send off the bottles for recycling - as glass made from old bottles costs much less energy than making new glass at the bottle factory. Or perhaps the bottles could simply be returned, to be used again. Enjoy a good discussion. If you decide to plan a "Save Energy Week", you will need to check the school electricity meter before and after the event.

SOUND PUZZLES
Sheet 35 AT4(iv):
Light seems to travel instantaneously. This is because its speed is a hard-to-imagine 300,000 kilometres per second. That's about 7 times round the Earth in the time it takes to say "Amazing!" If Jonathan's storm is one kilometre away, the sound of thunder will take three seconds to travel to his ears. That is after his eyes see the lightning. Emma's jet-plane will have travelled quite a distance before its sound reaches her ears, so if she looks in the direction where the sound seems to be coming from, she won't see the plane there. Ahmed is, of course, playing with the echo of his voice. An echo would not occur if sound did not take a little time to travel.

TEACHERS' NOTES

SOUND SENSE
Sheet 36 AT4(iv):
It is difficult to judge sound intensities without a scientific instrument, a fact that the children will discover for themselves, but practice in judging sound levels on this arbitrary scale will help to train the children's listening skills. Discuss the problem of noise pollution, with special reference to local places where the difficulty exists. What do the children think can and should be done about noise pollution?

MAGIC SHADOWS
Sheet 37 AT4(iv):
Manual and spatial dexterity are needed for this fascinating activity. Rays from a bright clear glass bulb, or from a projector, spread out and so cast giant shadows. Discuss the implications of these observations with the children, especially the idea that light rays usually travel in straight lines. Use the school projector to throw a bright light onto a screen in a darkened room, where the children can demonstrate their shadow magic.

BOUNCING BEAMS
Sheet 38 AT4(iv):
Angles made by the tubes and mirror will always look about the same, if the test is being carried out properly. Help the children to get it right. It is helpful to suggest that light rays bounce like a ball, when they are reflected. Of course, to refer to the laws of reflection is inappropriate. Just let this be a thoughtful game. Use the "light pulsometer" to compare the children's pulses. Remind the children that it is very dangerous to look directly at the sun.

SPACE MISSION
Sheet 39 AT4(v):
It should be possible to make and use this simple model in about an hour, with a small group of children. The whole point of this activity is to excite the children's sense of wonder about the immensity of space and the relatively small size of our home planet Earth. When the model is finished, if you look towards the "moon" and "sun" from the location of the "Earth", the sun and moon models should seem to be the same size, ignoring perspective, of course. This observation will help to explain how the moon can eclipse the sun.

ORANGE MOON
Sheet 40 AT4(v):
Help the children to appreciate how the other lunar shapes occur. Make certain that they realise that the apparent shape of the moon is a consequence of reflected sunlight reaching their eyes. They don't see the unlit portion of the moon. A moon shaped like a letter D is waxing (approaching the full moon phase). A moon shaped like a letter C is waning. The word "DOC" is a useful mnemonic.

BEANS AND BUGS
Sheet 41 AT4(ii):
These ideas are to give children opportunities to argue scientifically and will not necessarily lead to practical investigations (also see AT2(ii)). Perhaps tickling with a feather helps to cross pollinate the bean flowers more effectively. After all, there are fewer bees about nowadays. Gran objects because there are many factors other than heat which might have affected the bug, such as smell, the light, the movement of the match, its shape, etc. Discuss a conceivable fair test with the children. How could the bug's reaction to heat be tested, without the distraction of other variable factors?

THINK AGAIN
Sheet 42 AT4(ii):
The aim of these discussion pieces is to get children to appreciate different ways of thinking about ideas and inferences. A refrigerator pumps heat energy out into the room, warming up its surroundings. If the door is left open, the refrigerator simply recycles warm air, whilst actually adding heat from its motor. A light moving across the night sky is most likely to be something well-known, such as an aeroplane, a balloon with a light on it, or a distant satellite reflecting the sun's rays (as the moon does).